This book belongs to:

_____

_____

Contents

First published 2008 by Brown Watson
The Old Mill, 76 Fleckney Road,
Kibworth Beauchamp, Leic LE8 0HG

ISBN: 978 0 7097 1802 4

© 2008 Brown Watson, England
Reprinted 2008, 2009, 2010 (twice), 2012
Printed in Malaysia

EARLY READERS

Three Read With Me Stories

Stories by Gill Davies

Illustrations by:
Gill Guile, Stephen Holmes,
Jane Swift and Lawrie Taylor

Brown Watson

ENGLAND

MONKEY FUN

It is raining. Wet, wet rain falls . . . Plip! Plop! Splash!

The toys cannot go out into the garden to play.

"Never mind," says Monkey. "I will show you some funny tricks." First Monkey stands on his head. Then he throws lots of balls in the air. One hits Clown on the nose. Bash! Bump! Ow!

"Sorry," giggles Monkey.

Now Monkey does a dance. He jumps up and down. He kicks his legs.

Then he throws the balls into the air again . . .

One, two, three, four, five.

The toys cheer as Monkey dances and kicks and still catches the balls.

"You are very clever," say Duck and Daisy Doll and Blue Rabbit and Cool Cat.

Then Cool Cat shouts, "It has stopped raining. The sun is out. Now we can all go into the garden and play."

"Hooray!" says Monkey. "My arms are too tired to catch the balls any more."

He drops all the balls and rolls on the floor and giggles.

"Thank you, Monkey," says Blue Rabbit. "That was such good fun!"

KEY WORDS

balls	never
can	rain
cannot	really
five	sun
fun	the
garden	then
go	wet
in	will

WHAT CAN YOU SEE HERE?

duck

one ball

juggling

monkey

six balls

MAGIC TRICKS

Today Teddy is at a show.

Some teddy bears do a dance.

Teddy's friend Lollipop Bear sings and Sam Bear tells a funny story . . . but the best bit of the show is when Mr Magic does some clever tricks and finds a coin on the top of Teddy's head.

"How did you do that?" asks Teddy.

15

The next day, Teddy tries a trick with his friends.

"Look!" he says. "I am good at magic too."

When the other bears stare at Teddy's magic stick, he drops a coin into his hood.

"The coin has gone," he says. "It is magic!"

"Where is it?" ask the other teddy bears ... "How did you do that?"

Teddy grins.

Then he shakes the apple tree so that all the bears look at it and not at him.

While the bears all stare at the apple tree, Teddy finds the coin again.

"Look," he says. "Here it is!"

"Wow! Magic!" say the other bears. "How did you do that?"

Teddy just grins from ear to ear.

KEY WORDS

again	sings
apple	some
finds	story
funny	tell
girl	today
how	too
just	top
show	tree

WHAT CAN YOU SEE HERE?

coin

cloak

wand

apples

hat

COUNT YOUR EGGS

Duck lays an egg.

She is very happy. So she lays one, two, three more. Now she has four eggs.

Goose lays an egg – and she is very happy too. She lays one, two, three more. Now she has four eggs.

"Go away!" Duck quacks. "These are my eggs!"

Goose honks too, "Go away! These are my eggs!"

Duck and Goose take good care of their eggs.

They stay close by all the time. They keep the eggs warm. They sing to them.

They count the eggs to make sure they are all safe:
One . . . two . . . three . . . four.

Good. They are all here.

Then one day, the eggs go
POP!

Out come the ducklings:
One . . . two . . . three . . .
four.

Out come the goslings:
One . . . two . . . three . . .
four.

Duck and Goose are so happy.
The new babies play together
and are soon the very
best of friends.

KEY WORDS

an	my
are	now
best	one
egg	she
four	they
has	three
is	two
more	very

WHAT CAN YOU SEE HERE?

one goose

one duck

two goslings

three ducklings

four ducklings

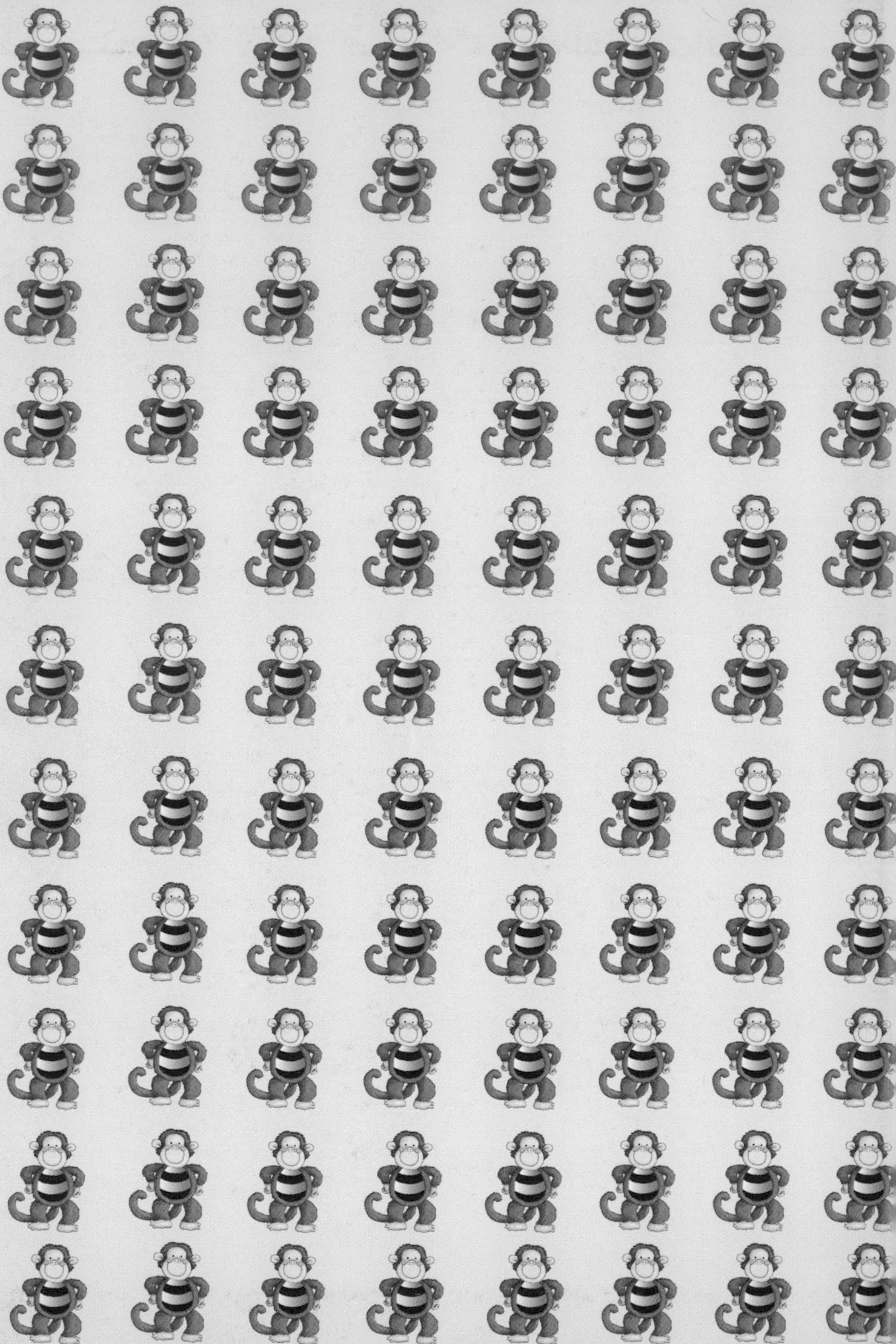